M000046263

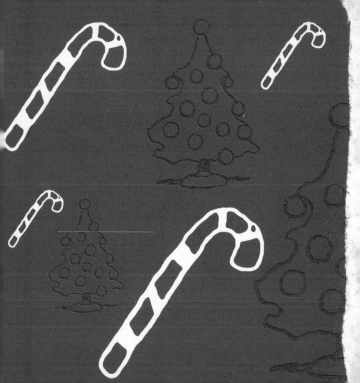

# Season's Greetings!

by
SCHULZ

CollinsPublishersSanFrancisco
*A Division of* HarperCollins*Publishers*

# I'm
# In The Mood For
# Christmas

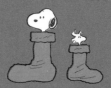

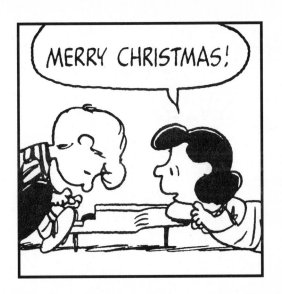

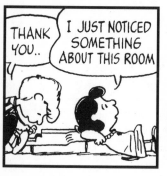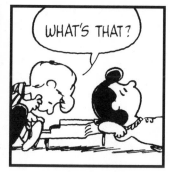

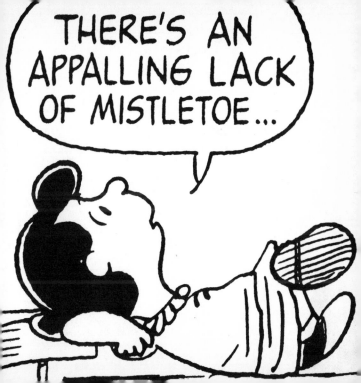

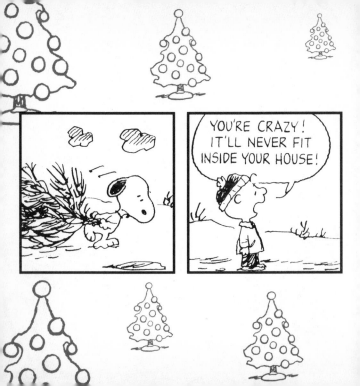

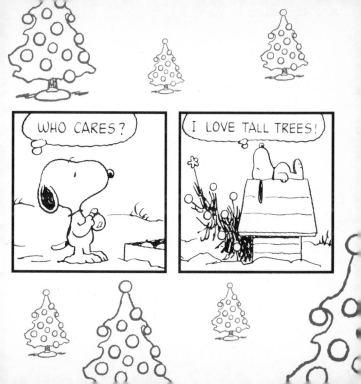

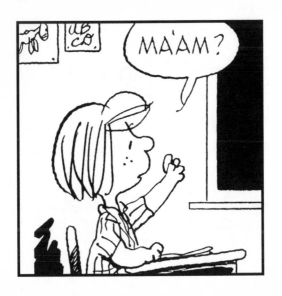

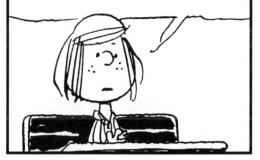

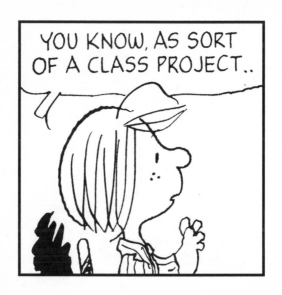

WE COULD START WITH MY MATH PAPER..

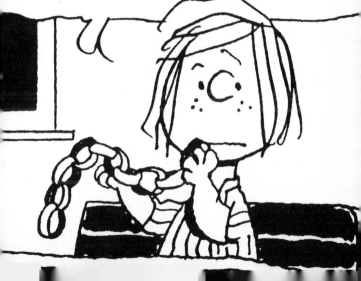

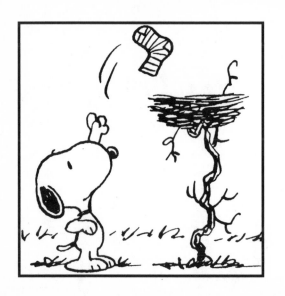

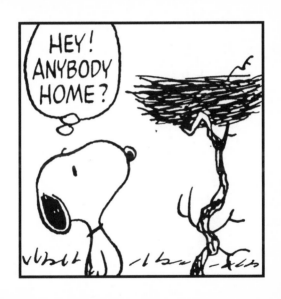

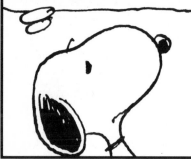

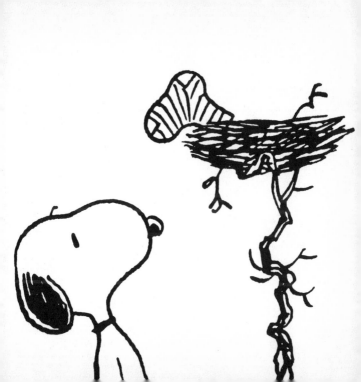

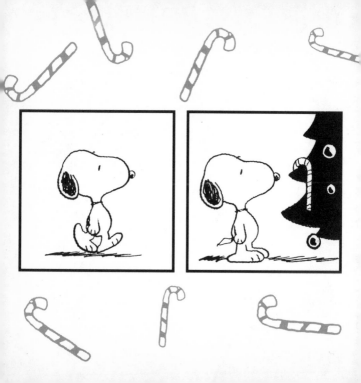

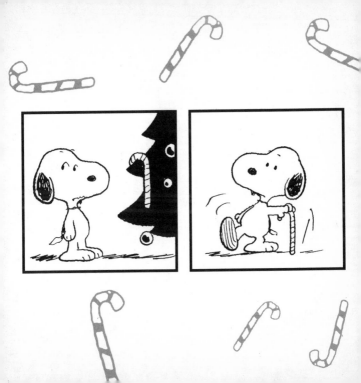

# Here
# Comes Santa
# Claus!

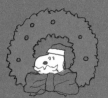

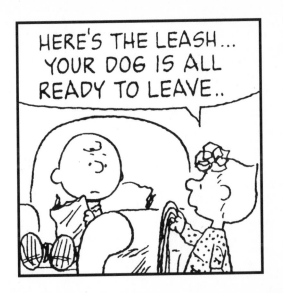

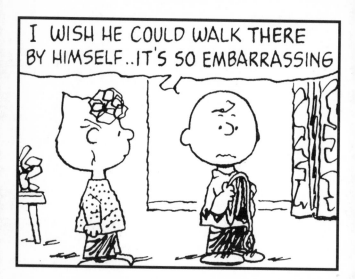

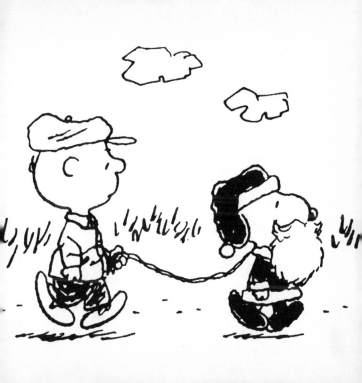

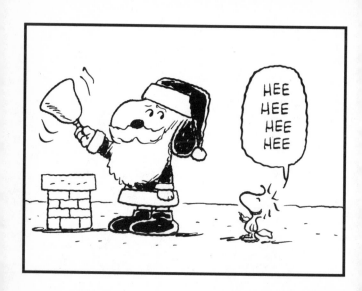

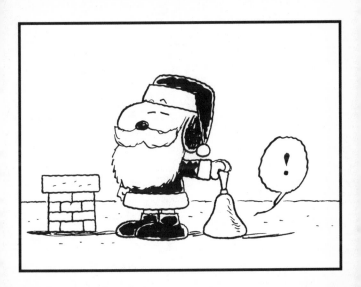

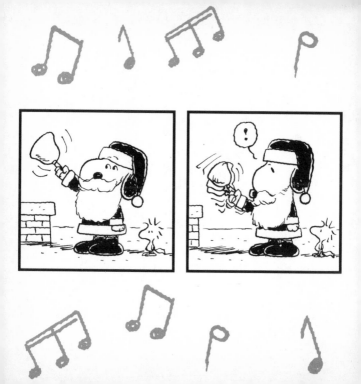

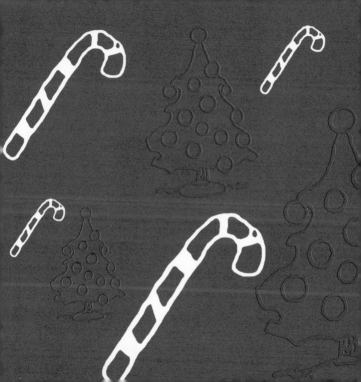

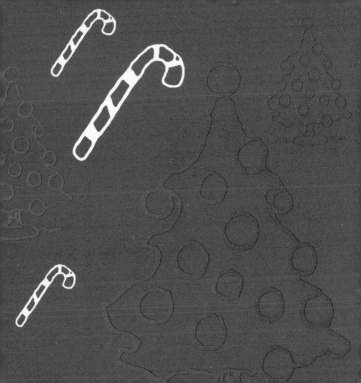